THIS BOOK BELONGS TO:

NAME: _____

PHONE: _____

IF LOST, PLEASE CALL ASAP

TO RETURN TO RIGHTFUL OWNER

CYDNEY-ELISE

"Cydney-Elise, are you still awake in there? You know tomorrow is a big day, you have to wake up early so I can do your hair" said mom. "Mommy, I can't believe tomorrow is the day. And the day is less than twenty-four hours away. What will I be when I grow up? I've given it no thought.

This is too abrupt, cried Cydney-Elise."

Mama please tell Mrs. Pennington that I definitely need more time.

To figure out which path to take and sort through which ladder to climb.

I need to search salaries and skills, duties and education. The more I think about it, the more I need a vacation.

My head is so full. I need to settle down. I've got fifteen hours to turn this thing around.

So what will I be when I grow up?

Hmmm let me see...

I could become a US Secretary of State like Condoleeza Rice. To be the President's Chief foreign affairs advisor, my input would have to be concise.

I could be like Michelle Obama and become a First Lady. Or I could be the President helping the homeless in America and in Haiti.

Maybe I'll be like Oprah Winfrey and become a billionaire. With my OWN talk show, magazine and Tv Network, I'd be able to help people everywhere.

I could train to be an Opera singer like the world famous Leontyne Price. To fill the entire Met Opera theater would take time, lots of training and good advice.

I could strive to be like Mae Jemison and become an Astronaut. I'd have to learn chemistry, engineering and even languages, I could become a polyglot.

I could be as graceful as Misty Copeland, the beautiful Prima Ballerina. I'd dance Swan Lake and the Nutcracker across a stage in Argentina.

I could work in ophthalmology like Dr. Patricia Bath. To identify sight lines and calculate prescriptions, I'll have to be pretty good at Math.

If I'm funny I can become a famous comedian like Wanda Sykes and Niecy Nash. I'll just hop on stage and tell some jokes and dash away with all the cash.

Or maybe I'll be an Olympic gymnast like Gabby Douglas or Simone Biles. I'd compete on Floor, Bars, Beam and Vault, scoring 10's all the while. Gymnastics isn't an easy sport. I'd need a high tolerance for pain. But if I win a Gold medal for my Country then it would not have been in vain.

I could even become a famous actress. That would be the funnest of them all. Like my Grandma CCH Pounder-Kone', playing different characters would be a ball. The idea of winning an Oscar or an Emmy would have me tingling with anticipation. But if I were being perfectly honest it would be an honor just to get a nomination.

I could be like Venus and Serena Williams and become an athletic tennis Pro. Then little girls just like you will want to be like me when they grow. Venus and Serena started from humble beginnings and managed to build an empire. If I want to leave my family a dynasty, it has to start with a never ending desire.

These women are beyond phenomenal
in their own right.

I will be sure when I grow up it is
about my accomplishments they
will write.

Their contributions are all documented.
They are a well-known fact. And the
women who achieved them are just like
me. They are Proud and they are Black.

So what will I be when I grow up?

I CAN BE ANYTHING...

                                    And I will

MICHELLE OBAMA
First Lady/Attorney/Writer (1964-)

Michelle Obama was born Michelle LaVaughn Robinson on January 17, 1964 in Chicago, Illinois to parents, Fraser and Marion Robinson. Michelle and her brother Craig were raised with an emphasis on education. They both learned to read by the age of four and skipped the second grade. By the sixth grade she learned French and completed accelerated courses in biology. Michelle attended Whitney M. Young Magnet High School for Gifted children where she served as the student government treasurer and graduated in 1981 as the class salutatorian.

Michelle attended Princeton University graduating cum laude in 1985 with a B.A. in Sociology and then went on to study Law at Harvard Law School where she was awarded her J.D. in 1988.

After Law school, Michelle worked in the Chicago branch of the firm Sidley Austin, in the area of marketing and intellectual properties. It was there that she met her future husband, Barack Obama. Barack proposed after two years of dating and the couple married on October 3, 1992 at Trinity United Church of Christ. Their eldest daughter, Malia was born in 1998 and Sasha in 2001.

Michelle decided to leave corporate law and pursue a career in public service in 1991. She began working as an assistant commissioner of planning and development of the City of Chicago for Mayor Richard Daley, then Executive director for the Chicago office of Public Allies in 1993. In 1996, Michelle became the associate dean of student services at the University of Chicago. Starting in 2002 she began working for the University of Chicago hospital as executive director of community relations and external affairs. By 2005 Michelle was appointed vice president for community and external affairs at the University of Chicago Medical Center where she continued to work until shortly before her husband's inauguration as the 44th President of the United States on January 20, 2009. Barack Obama was re-elected for a second term as US President on November 2, 2012. As First Lady of the United States, Michelle Obama's attention was focused on helping working women balance career, supporting military families and encouraging National service.

Michelle Obama fully supported the organic-food movement, instructing the White House kitchens to only prepare organic food for the guests and her family. In March of 2009, Michelle planted a 1,100 square foot garden of fresh vegetables with 23 fifth graders from a local school in Washington DC. They also installed beehives on the South Lawn of the White House. Michelle Obama placed fighting childhood obesity near the top of her agenda. Michelle remained committed to her health-and-wellness causes and in 2012 she introduced a new fitness program for kids as part of her Let's Move initiative. As a part of her mission to promote healthy eating, Michelle released a book called American Grown: The Story of the White House Kitchen Garden and Gardens Across America putting her message in print.

Michelle was featured in Essence magazine as one of "25 of the World's Most Inspiring Women" in May of 2006. Michelle was also included in 02138 magazine as number 58 in "The Harvard 100," a yearly list of the the school's most influential alumni. Michelle Obama, America's First Lady, was also named "The Most Powerful Woman in the World in the Forbes 100 list in 2012. Michelle Obama made the Vanity Fair's best dressed-list two years in a row as well as People magazine's 2008 best-dressed list. She also appeared twice on the cover of Vogue magazine.

OPRAH WINFREY
American Media Mogul (1954-)

Oprah Gail Winfrey was born in Kosciusko, Mississippi to Vernita Lee and Vernon Winfrey on January 29, 1954. Oprah's parents separated soon after she was born and she was raised under the strict guidance of her maternal grandmother on a farm. She was given the opportunity to address her church congregation about "when Jesus rose on Easter Day" when she was two years old. By two and a half she had learned to read. On Oprah's first day of kindergarten she wrote a convincing note to her teacher stating that she belonged in the first grade. Oprah immediately skipped to first grade and promoted to the third grade the following year. At six years old Oprah moved to a Milwaukee ghetto to live with her mother and two half-brothers. At the age of 12 she was sent to live with her father in Nashville, Tennessee.

Oprah began to make speeches at churches and social gatherings and on one occasion earned five hundred dollars for her speech. This is when Oprah knew that she wanted to be "paid to talk." Although Oprah moved around a lot she was an excellent student, participating in the drama club, debate club and the student council. Winfrey also won a full scholarship to

Tennessee State University for winning an Elks Club speaking contest. She was invited to a White House Conference on Youth the following year and crowned Miss Fire Prevention by WVOL, a local Nashville radio station. The station then hired Oprah to read the afternoon newscasts. During her freshman year at Tennessee State, Winfrey became Miss Black Nashville and Miss Tennessee. The Nashville (CBS) affiliate offered Winfrey a job twice which she declined to accept, but finally took her speech teachers advice, who reminded her that job offers from CBS were "the reason people go to college." The show aired each evening on WTVF-TV. Oprah Winfrey was Nashville's first Black female co-anchor of the evening news. Oprah was only nineteen years old and still a sophomore in college. After graduation, Oprah was scheduled to do local news updates during Good Morning America but was soon moved to the morning talk show, Baltimore Is Talking with cohost Richard Sher on WJZ-TV in Baltimore, Maryland.

 After seven years on the show, Winfrey was spotted by the general manager of WLS-TV, (ABC's) Chicago affiliate in an audition tape sent in by her producer, Debra DiMaio. At the time Oprah's ratings in Baltimore were better than the national talk-show host, Phil Donahue. She and DiMaio were hired. In January 1984, Winfrey moved to Chicago, Illinois and took over as anchor on a morning talk show that was consistently last in the ratings called A.M. Chicago. Oprah changed the show's emphasis from traditional women's issues to current and controversial topics. After one month her show had even ratings with Donahue's program and within three months had inched ahead. In September of 1985, the program was expanded to one hour and renamed the Oprah Winfrey Show. As a result, Donahue moved to New York City. It was this year that Quincy Jones (1933-) took notice to Winfrey on television and thought she would be excellent for a movie he was coproducing with director Steven Spielberg (1946-). The film was called The Color Purple which was based on the Alice Walker (1944-) novel. After the success of the Color Purple, Winfrey's show skyrocketed. In September 1985 the distributor King World bought the syndication rights to air the program in one hundred thirty-eight cities, a record for first-time syndication. Winfrey won her time slot by 31 percent, drew twice the Chicago audience as Donahue and carried the top ten markets in the United States. Oprah Winfrey was honored as Best Talk Show Host and The Oprah Winfrey Show won several Emmys for Best Talk Show. In August 1986, Winfrey formed her own production company, Harpo, Inc., to produce the topics that she wanted to see produced.

On September 17, 1996 Winfrey announced she wanted "to get the country reading." She encouraged her fans to run to the stores to purchase the book she had selected. They would then discuss it together on the air the following month. This on-air reading club ensured Winfrey as the most powerful book marketer in the United States. After a six-year run with her book club Winfrey decided to no longer have the book club as a monthly feature. (Info at Notable biographies)

Serena Williams Biography
Pro Tennis Player, Entrepreneur (1981-)

Serena Jameka Williams was born on September 26, 1981 and is the youngest of Richard and Oracene Williams' five daughters. She is an American professional tennis player currently ranked as the 11th best player in the world by the Women's Tennis Association (WTA). Williams began intensive tennis training at age three and withstood the rigors of daily two-hour practices from her father. Williams has won 23 Grand Slam Titles, 14 Grand Slam doubles titles with elder sister Venus and several Olympic gold medals. Venus and Serena, with their signature style and play changed the look of their sport. They overwhelmed their opponents with sheer power and athletic ability

In 2009, Venus and Serena purchased shares of the Miami Dolphins to become the first Black women to own part of an NFL team.

In December 2016, Williams became engaged to Reddit co-founder Alexis Ohanian. On November 16, 2017, Williams and Ohanian were married at the Contemporary Arts Center in New Orleans, Louisiana. Williams gave birth to daughter Alexis Olympia Ohanian Jr. on September 1, 2017. The tennis great posted a photo with her baby on Instagram and shared the journey of her pregnancy in a video posted on her website and on YouTube. Williams revealed in the cover story for the February 2018 edition of Vogue, major health complications that resulted from childbirth.

In June of 2017 *Forbes* magazine put Serena Williams' net worth at $27 million. Her career $84 million in prize winnings is almost $50 million more than any other women's tennis player. She also has over a dozen endorsements including Intel, Tempur-Pedic, Nike, Beats By Dre, Gatorade and JP Morgan Chase.

Venus Williams Biography

Tennis Player, Athlete (1980-)

Born on June 17, 1980, in Lynwood, California, Venus Ebony Starr Williams learned to play tennis on the public courts of Los Angeles. She rose from a tough childhood in Compton, California to become a champion women's tennis player and four-time Olympic gold medalist. By the age of 10, Williams' serve topped 100 miles per hour. After turning professional in 1994, she won seven Grand Slam titles, including five Wimbledon championships and an Olympic gold medal in singles play. She also teamed up with sister Serena Williams to win 14 Grand Slam doubles championships, boosting her victory total even after being diagnosed with an autoimmune disease in 2011. In 2000, she won both the U.S. Open and Wimbledon, paving the way for her to in a $40 million Reebok contract.

Off the court, Venus Williams cultivated a varied number of interests. She's pursued art classes, and earned a certificate in interior design. She started a clothing line called EleVen, as well as a collection of women's apparel for Wilson's Leather. In addition, she launched her own interior design company called V*Starr Interiors, which works on residential projects throughout the country.

In 2009, Venus and Serena became the first Black women to buy shares of an NFL team when they joined the ownership group of the Miami Dolphins.

The following year, Venus co-authored the New York Times bestseller *Come To Win: Business Leaders, Artists, Doctors, and Other Visionaries on How Sports Can Help You Top Your Profession*, in which she interviewed such successful individuals as Richard Branson and Condoleezza Rice about their early athletic experiences.

The tennis champion has also been active in a number of social causes, including working closely with UNESCO on promoting gender equality throughout the world.

MAE JEMISON
Doctor, Scientist, Astronaut (1956-)

Mae C. Jemison was born on October 17, 1956 in Decatur, Alabama. She is the youngest child of Charlie Jemison, and Dorothy (Green) Jemison, an elementary school teacher. Chicago is the city that Mae considers her hometown. Jemison spent a considerable amount of time in her school library throughout her early school years reading about all aspects of science, mainly astronomy. Her parents were very encouraging and supportive of her abilities and talents. While in school at Morgan Park High, Jemison became convinced she wanted to pursue a career in biomedical engineering. Upon graduation in 1973, she received a National Achievement Scholarship which she used to attend Stanford University. At Stanford she became involved in theatre productions and dance and served as head of the Black Student Union as she had been in high school. In 1977, she received a Bachelor of Science degree in chemical engineering and upon graduation she entered Cornell University Medical College. While there she expanded her horizons studying in Kenya and Cuba and working at a Cambodian refugee camp in Thailand.

In 1981, after Jemison obtained her M.D., she later worked as a general practitioner. For the next two and a half years that followed, she taught and did medical research as the area Peace Corps medical officer for Sierra Leone and Liberia. In 1985 after returning to the United States, Jemison changed her career and decided to follow her long time childhood dream. That October she applied for admission to NASA's astronaut training program. The selection process was delayed by the Challenger disaster of January 1986. Jemison reapplied a year later and was one of the 15 candidates chosen from a field of about 2,000.

Mae C. Jemison became the first Black woman to be admitted into the NASA astronaut training program. After just over a year of training, Jemison became the first Black woman astronaut, earning the title of science mission specialist. This job would make her responsible for conducting crew-related scientific experiments on the space shuttle. On September 12, 1992, Jemison finally flew into space with six other astronauts aboard the Endeavour on mission STS47, becoming the first Black woman in space. Jemison conducted experiments on motion sickness and weightlessness on the crew and herself during her eight days in space. She spent more than 190 hours in space before her return to Earth on September 20, 1992. Following her historic flight, Jemison noted that society should recognize how much both women and members of other minority groups can contribute if given the opportunity.

Jemison received a number of accolades in recognition of her accomplishments, including the 1988 Essence Science and Technology Award, several honorary doctorates and she was named Gamma Sigma Gamma Woman of the Year in 1990. She received the Ebony Black Achievement Award in 1992 and a Montgomery Fellowship from Dartmouth College in 1993. In 1992, the Mae C. Jemison Academy, an alternative public school in Detroit, Michigan, was named after her.

Jemison has been a member of several prominent organizations, including the American Association for the Advancement of Science, the American Medical Association, the American Chemical Society and she served on the board of directors of the World Sickle Cell Foundation from 1990 to 1992. She also served as an honorary board member of the Center for the Prevention of Childhood Malnutrition and as an advisory committee member of the American Express Geography Competition.

In March of 1993, Jemison left NASA's astronaut corps and accepted a teaching fellowship at Dartmouth. She also established a company that seeks to research, develop and market advanced technologies called the Jemison Group.

MISTY COPELAND
Prima Ballerina (1982-)

On September 10, 1982 in Kansas City, Missouri, dancer, Misty Copeland was born. She was the fourth of six siblings of mixed ethnic heritage. Copeland endured a troubled home life to find her way to dance. She eventually studied under the guidance of California ballet instructor Cynthia "Cindy" Bradley who realized the Copeland was a prodigy.

While her dancing life was blossoming, Misty's home life became more difficult. It was at this point that her mother, Sylvia Delacerna and Bradley decided that 13-year-old Copeland should move in with her teacher's family. This allowed Copeland to continue her training as she entered the public spotlight as a promising up-and-coming performer

Copeland's mother demanded that she return home after having attended a summer intensive program on scholarship at the San Francisco Ballet. A battle ensued between Delcerna and Bradley. With accompanying coverage from local media, Copeland began looking into legal separation from her biological parent at 15 years old. Ultimately the request was dropped with Copeland returning to live with her mother by police escort.

Copeland refused to let go of her career. She took classes at the Lauridsen Ballet Centre followed by another summer intensive in 1999 at the renowned American Ballet Theatre. In September of 2000, she joined ABT's studio company becoming part of its corps de ballet the following year. By 2007, she reached the rank of ABT soloist

Copeland continued pursuing her passion and developing her skills in many different repertoires. She did this while battling some pretty severe injuries. Due to a delayed onset of puberty, Copeland faced a vertebral fracture that demanded time off of dance at the beginning of her ABT career. This injury caused her to have to wear a brace for practically the entire day. She had to temporarily stop dancing again years later to recuperate from stress fractures to her left shin.

In June 2015, Copeland became the first Black woman to dance with ABT in the dual role of Odette and Odile in Pyotry Ilycih Tchaikovsky's Swan Lake. By June 30, 2015, Copeland became the first African-American performer to be appointed an ABT principal dancer. A monumental achievement covered the world over.

Copeland's success via the guidance of manager Gilda Squire afforded her the ability to forge a career outside of the classic traditions of ballet. In 2013 not only did Copeland have her own calendar, a spot on Prince's Welcome 2 tour, a guest appearance on So You Think You Can Dance, endorsement deals with American Express and COACH, Copeland was one of the stars of Under Armour's "I Will What I Want" video campaign, with her clip receiving more than 8 million views and counting. Copeland was also a member of President Barack Obama's Council on Fitness, Sports & Nutrition. Publishing two works in 2014, the ballerina also became a tour de force in the literary world: New York Times best selling memoir Life in Motion: An Unlikely Ballerina, with journalist Charisse Jones as co-writer, and her award-winning children's picture book Firebird, illustrated by Christopher Myers. In May of 2016, a Copeland inspired Barbie doll was released wearing a costume reminiscent of the one she wore in Firebird. The doll is a part of Barbie's Sheroes program which honors female heroes who break boundaries.

On a personal note, Misty Copeland married her long time beau of 10 years, attorney Olu Evans in Laguna Beach, California on July 31, 2016.

Gabby Douglas Biography

Athlete, Gymnast (1995–)

Gabrielle Christina Victoria Douglas was born on December 31, 1995 to Timothy Douglas and Natalie Hawkins. Douglas' first experience with gymnastics came at the age of three when she perfected a straight cartwheel using a technique that she'd learned from her older sister, Arielle. By age four she'd taught herself how to do a one-handed cartwheel.

She began formal gymnastics training at six years old and only two years later, she was named a Virginia State Gymnastics Champion.

When Douglas turned 14, she left her family and hometown, and moved to West Des Moines, Iowa, with Travis and Missy Parton who had volunteered to be her host family. It was in West Des Moines, Iowa where Douglas trained with renowned coach Liang Chow who was known for molding American gymnast Shawn Johnson into a world champion and Olympic gold medalist.

Douglas made her debut on the national scene at the 2010 Nastia Liukin SuperGirl Cup in a televised meet held in Massachussetts, placing fourth all-around. In the 2010 CoverGirl Classic in Chicago, Illinois, her first elite meet, Douglas placed sixth on vault, third on the balance beam and ninth all-around in the junior division. Douglas went on to win the silver medal on balance beam and fourth all-around at the 2010 U.S. Junior National Championships. She then took the uneven bars title at the 2010 Pan American Championships. She placed fifth all-around and her performance helped the U.S. team win the gold medal.

Douglas was a member of the U.S. team that won the gold medal in the team finals at the 2011 World Artistic Gymnastics Championships in Tokyo, Japan. She was also selected as a member of the national team that represented the United States at the 2012 Summer Olympics in London when she won the 2012 Olympic Trials in San Jose, California.

Douglas and the other members of the U.S. Olympic women's gymnastics team-McKayla Maroney, Aly Raisman, Kyla Ross and Jordan Wieber-took home a team gold medal. This was the first gold medal for the American women's gymnastics team since 1996.

Gabby Douglas, is an American gymnast who became the first Black American in Olympic history to win the individual all-around event at the 2012 Summer Games. Douglas also won team gold medals at the 2012 and 2016 Summer Olympics. She was featured on the cover of Sports Illustrated in early July of 2012, along with the rest of the U.S. Olympic women's gymnastics team, and on one of five covers released by TIME Magazine that same month. She was also a featured Olympian on Kellogg's special edition box of Wheaties corn flakes.

When Douglas earned a spot on the 2016 Olympic team she became the first reigning all-around Olympic champion to return to compete in a second Olympic Games since Nadia Comaneci in 1980. She and teammate Aly Raisman, both members of the gold medal-winning team in 2012 were the first American women gymnasts to return to the Olympics since Dominique Dawes and Amy Chow in 2000.

In 2016, Gabby Douglas helped "The Final Five" grab the gold again with her impressive performance on the uneven bars, for which she scored 15.766. In 2016, Gabby Douglas unveiled a Barbie Shero doll just before the Summer Olympics in Rio.

Simone Biles Biography

Athlete, Gymnast (1997-)

Simone Biles was born on March 14, 1997 in Columbus, Ohio. Due to their mother's struggle with substance abuse, Simone and her sister Adria, were raised by their grandmother Nellie and their grandfather Ron. The two sisters were eventually adopted by their grandparents. Throughout Biles's rise in the world of competitive gymnastics, grandmother Nellie was a constant source of support.

At an early age Biles discovered her gymnastics abilities while on a field trip with her daycare group. Coach Ronnie took notice while Simone playfully imitated other gymnasts. The gym sent a letter home requesting her to join the gymnastics or tumbling program. Soon enough Biles was on her way to developing those natural gifts. Simone emerged as a champion and a force to be reckoned with in the sport of gymnastics. Biles frequently executed what has become her signature move, a double-flip with a half-twist.

Biles has claimed many historic firsts. In 2013 she became the first Black American female athlete to win Gold in the all-around category. In 2015 she became the first woman to win her third consecutive world all around title, giving her a record 10 gold medals at the international competition. She also became the first woman to win back-to-back Olympic all-around and world titles in two decades. She became one of America's top gymnasts having won a combined total of twenty-five Olympic and World Championship medals. Simone Biles is the most decorated American gymnast and the third most decorated female gymnast in history.

Biles joined the cast of the 24th season of *Dancing with the Stars in 2017* on which she was paired with pro Sasha Farber. The Olympic champion was eliminated during the semifinals in May despite impressing the judges with her moves.

Dr. Patricia Bath

Inventor, Doctor, Educator (1942-)

Dr. Patricia Bath was born in Harlem, New York, on November 4, 1942, to Rupert Bath, the first black motorman for the New York City subway system, and Gladys Bath, a housewife and domestic worker. Gladys used her salary to save money for her children's education. She piqued her young daughters interest in science by buying her a chemistry set. As a result, Bath worked hard on her intellectual pursuits and, at the age of 16, became one of only a few students to attend a cancer research workshop sponsored by the National Science Foundation. The program head, Dr. Robert Bernard, was so impressed with Bath's discoveries during the project that he incorporated her findings in a scientific paper he presented at a conference. The publicity surrounding her discoveries earned Bath the *Mademoiselle* magazine's Merit Award in 1960. After graduating from high school in only two years, Bath headed to Hunter College, where she earned a bachelor's degree in 1964. She then attended Howard University to pursue a medical degree. Bath graduated with honors from Howard in 1968, and accepted an internship at Harlem Hospital shortly afterward. The following year, she also began pursuing a fellowship in ophthalmology at Columbia University. Through her studies there, she discovered that Black Americans were twice as likely to suffer from blindness than other patients to which she attended, and eight times more likely to develop glaucoma. Her research led to her development of a community ophthalmology system, which increased the amount of eye care given to those who were unable to afford treatment.

Dr. Patricia Bath became the first Black American to complete a residency in ophthalmology in 1973. Two years later, she became the first female faculty member in the Department of Ophthalmology at UCLA's Jules Stein Eye Institute. In 1976, Bath co-founded the American Institute for the Prevention of Blindness, which established that "eyesight is a basic human right." By 1983, Bath had helped create the Ophthalmology Residency Training program at UCLA-Drew, which she also chaired—becoming, in addition to her other firsts, the first woman in the nation to hold such a position. In 1986, Bath invented the Laserphaco Probe. Harnessing laser technology, the device created a less painful and more precise treatment of cataracts. She patented the device in 1988, becoming the first Black female doctor to receive a medical patent for a medical purpose. (She also holds patents in Japan, Canada and Europe.) With her Laserphaco Probe, Bath was able to help restore the sight of individuals who had been blind for more than 30 years. In 1993, Bath retired from her position at the UCLA Medical Center and became an honorary member of its medical staff. That same year, she was named a "Howard University Pioneer in Academic Medicine." Among her many roles in the medical field, Bath is a strong advocate of telemedicine, which uses technology to provide medical services in remote areas.

Wanda Sykes Biography
Television Actress, Comedian (1964–)

Wanda Sykes was born in Portsmouth, Virginia on March 7, 1964, to her father, who was a colonel that worked at the Pentagon and her mother, a banker. Sykes also has an older brother, Harry. They grew up in Gambrills, Maryland, near Washington, D.C. Sykes enjoyed a comfortable middle-class childhood and attended Arundel High School. She went on to get a bachelor's degree in marketing from Hampton University in Virginia before moving on to a government job in the D.C. area. Her position as a procurement officer at the National Security Agency didn't particularly suit her. The comedian and actress started out doing stand-up on the road. She went on to make numerous appearances on the big and small screens, and won 9 Emmy nominations including one for her own stand-up special. In 2009, she brought her intelligent, political humor to the White House, becoming the first Black woman, and first openly gay comedian, to perform at the White House Correspondents' Association Dinner. Since then, Sykes has appeared on such shows as *Black-ish* and *Alpha House*.

As it turned out, Sykes was much better suited for the stage than for government bureaucracy. After five years of playing comedy clubs in the D.C. area, Sykes was ready to quit her day job and make a life in comedy. Sykes had found something that she loved. At 28, she was finally on the road to becoming one of the most recognizable comedians of our day. The next big step in her life was a move to New York. Sykes' current body of work spans TV, film, writing for Variety, music or comedy, voice-over work, a late night Talk Show, an author and Stand-Up. She shows no signs of slowing down.

Even with all of her visible roles, Sykes has succeeded in staying highly protective of her family and personal life. She and her wife, Alex, have twins, Olivia and Lucas, but Sykes won't go so far as to give her wife's last name or even her job. This is Sykes' second marriage; she married record producer David Hall in 1991, just before her move to New York, and they remained married until 1998. Raised in a traditional, religious community, Sykes knew that she was gay, but felt compelled to live life as a straight woman. She experienced the end of her marriage to Hall as a "liberating moment" and began dating women.

Niecy Nash Biography

Comedian, Television Actress, Television Host (1970–)

Niecy Nash was born on February 23, 1970, in Los Angeles, California. She is a comedian, actress and TV personality. She spent her early years in St. Louis, Missouri. There Nash discovered her life's dream when she was 5 years old. As she explained to the *St. Louis Post-Dispatch*, she was watching television with her grandmother when "a beautiful black woman" appeared on screen. The woman in question turned out to be entertainer Lola Falana, and Nash "knew right then that's what I wanted to be. I wanted to be black, fabulous and on TV." Nash moved back to California around the age of 8. When she was 15, she nearly lost her mother. Her mother had been shot by her boyfriend, but she managed to recover from her injuries. Nash's younger brother, however, was later a victim of gun violence. He was shot to death at school. After her brother's death, Nash watched her mother sink into a deep depression. She started telling jokes to her mother to help raise her spirit. Nash told *People* magazine "That's when I realized comedy was a gift."

Nash earned a degree in Theater from California State University, Dominguez Hills, but she had a tough time landing parts after graduation. Her first big break came when she landed a role on the 1995 film *Boys on the Side* starring Whoopi Goldberg and Drew Barrymore. She went on to appear in Robert Altman's 1999 dramatic comedy *Cookie's Fortune*. On the small screen, Nash started with guest appearances on such shows as *Party of Five* and *City of Angels*. She first rose to fame with the comedy *Reno 911!* in 2003 and has worked steadily ever since. The show was a popular spoof of the documentary series *Cops*. On this sitcom, Nash brought the laughs as Deputy Raineesha Williams. She also landed a recurring role as comedian Bernie Mac's sister on *The Bernie Mac Show* around this time.

Nash used her comedic skills to tackle reality TV as well. She became the host of *Clean House*, a show that helped homeowners cut down on their clutter. Nash also did voice work for a number of animated series, including *Kid Notorious* and *American Dad!*. In 2008, she starred in her own sitcom, *Do Not Disturb*, co-starring with Jerry O'Connell. This series proved to be short lived, but Nash never slowed down for a second. Nash has three children, son Dominic and daughters Donielle and Dia, from her first marriage to Don Nash. The pair divorced in 2007. In 2011, Niecy married electrical engineer Jay Tucker. Their nuptials became the subject of a TV special entitled *Niecy Nash's Wedding Bash*. TV viewers were able to follow the couple's efforts to blend their families together (Tucker has a son of his own) in *Leave It to Niecy* in 2012. In 2010, Nash put on her dancing shoes to compete on *Dancing With the Stars*. She didn't win her season, but she added to her growing fan base. Two years later, Nash began starring in the TV comedy *The Soul Man* with Cedric the Entertainer. She also had a leading role in the HBO hospital sitcom *Getting On*. The role earned Nash her first Emmy nomination. In 2014, Nash made guest appearances on *The Mindy Project*. In 2015 she moved on to the horror comedy *Scream Queens* with Emma Roberts and Jamie Lee Curtis.

LEONTYNE PRICE
Singer (1927-)

Mary Violet Leontyne Price was born on February 10, 1927 in Laurel, Mississippi to carpenter, James Anthony Price and Kate Baker Price, a midwife with a beautiful singing voice. From a very young age Price showed an interest in music and was encouraged by her parents. She began formal music training at the age of 5 and spent much of her time singing in the choir at St. Paul Methodist Church. She traveled at the age of 9 with her mother to Jackson, Mississippi, to attend a recital by contralto Marian Anderson and Price found additional inspiration. She attended Oak Park Vocational High School where she was a member of the glee club and also a standout pianist. She then enrolled at the College of Education and Industrial Arts in Wilberforce, Ohio. It was there that she began focusing her studies on music education. She was encouraged by faculty later to switch her concentration to voice. Price headed to New York City upon graduation to attend The Juilliard School on a full scholarship.

Price studied under the tutelage of her beloved vocal instructor, Florence Page Kimball at Juilliard. Price landed feature roles in many of the school's operas with her beautiful lyric soprano voice. In a student production of Giuseppe Verdi's Falstaff, Price's performance in the role of Alice Ford was witnessed by composer Virgil Thomson who leapt at the chance to bring her into one of his productions. Leontyne Price made her Broadway debut in 1952 as St. Cecilia in the revival of Virgil Thomson's Four Saints in Three Acts. At the time Leontyne Price was not yet known for her operatic talents but immediately following the show's three-week engagement, she was cast in a touring production of George Gershwin's Porgy and Bess. Price gained acclaim and dazzled audiences with her flawless vocal interpretations and her stunning portrayal of Bess over the next two years. She married co-star William Warfield during her tour with the show but their busy professional careers led them to divorce in the early 1970's.

Price then starred in the NBC Opera Theatre's TV production of Giacomo Puccini's Tosca. A string of television operas featuring Price followed this performance. At the San Francisco Opera House, Price took on the role of Madame Lidoine in Francis Poulenc's Dialogues de Carmelites in her opera stage debut. The moving performance marked the commencement of her rise to fame in the serious opera community. Price had reached stardom at home as well as on an international level by 1958, wowing European audiences at famous venues such as La Scala in Milan and the Covent Garden in England.

By 1961, Price's debut performance of Leonora in II Trovatore at New York City's Metropolitan Opera House was such a huge success that it marked the beginning of her residency as one of the opera's principal sopranos. She flourished as a prima donna at the Met, starring in roles such as Minnie in La Fanciulla del West, Cio-Cio-San in Madame Butterfly but most notably, as Cleopatra in Anthony and Cleopatra.

37-year-old Price was awarded the Presidential Medal of Freedom by Lyndon B. Johnson in September of 1964. She became a National Medal of Arts recipient two decades later in 1985. Price earned more than a dozen Grammy Awards and numerous honors throughout her illustrious career. In a profession where limited opportunities existed for someone with her background, Leontyne Price amassed an impressive legacy, achieving stardom as a woman of color during a time of segregation in America.

At the Met in 1985 Price delivered her operatic farewell in the titular role of Aida, which was telecast and hailed as one of the most successful opera performances in Met's history. For the next dozen years, Price continued to perform recitals before retiring from the stage. In October 2001, Price made a brief exit from retirement to sing at a concert honoring victims of the September 11 terrorist attacks. Price became one of the first internationally recognized African-American opera stars.

Condoleezza Rice Biography
US National Security Advisor (1954 -)

Condoleezza Rice was born on November 14, 1954 in Birmingham, Alabama. The only child of a Presbyterian minister and a teacher, Rice grew up surrounded by racism in the segregated South.

She earned her bachelor's degree in political science from the University of Denver in 1974; her master's from the University of Notre Dame in 1975; and her Ph.D. from the University of Denver's Graduate School of International Studies in 1981.

In 1993, Rice became the first woman and the first black woman to serve as provost of Stanford University—a post she held for six years. During that time, she also served as the university's chief budget and academic officer.

In 2001, Rice was appointed national security adviser by President George W. Bush, becoming the first black woman (and second woman) to hold the post, and went on to become the first black woman to serve as U.S. Secretary of State.

That same year, she joined Stanford University as a political science professor—a position that she has held for more than three decades and plans to soon return to, full-time, according to a statement she made in 2012.

She became the first woman and first black American to serve as provost of Stanford University.

CCH POUNDER-KONE'

CCH Pounder-Kone' was born Carol Christine Hilaria in 1952 on Christmas Day in Georgetown, British Guyana. At an early age her parents moved to the States while she and her sister attended boarding school in Britain where they were introduced to art and the classics. Following her high school graduation, CCH studied at Ithaca College in New York where her acting talents were discovered. Shortly after her regional and classical repertory theater training, she began earning roles in productions such as "The Mighty Gents" with Morgan Freeman at the New York Shakespeare Festival and her Broadway debut "Open Admissions". In the late 1970's her preference for a warmer climate led her to move to Hollywood in California.

After bit roles in All That Jazz (1979) and I'm Dancing as Fast as I can (1982) she achieved cult status in the art-house film Bagdad Café (1987). But Pounder's notability and distinction came with television. Most commonly known for her understated intensity, CCH was typically cast as a strong-minded and confident professional which earned her an Emmy nomination for her role on the hospital drama/TV series ER (1994). Pounder has lended her talents to a number of highly acclaimed dramas. including Numb3rs (2005), (The Shield (2002-2008) earned her a Satellite Award for Best Actress as well as one Emmy and Image Award nomination, Law & Order: Special Victims Unit (2001-2010), Sons of Anarchy (2013-2014), NCIS New Orleans (2014-2019) just to name a few.

Pounder portrayed the role of Sister Abigail in Orphan (2009) in which David Leslie Johnson-McGoldrick wrote the part specifically with her in mind. CCH has appeared in a number of films that were nominated for the Best Picture Oscar: All That Jazz (1979), Prizzi's Honor (1985) and Avatar (2009). CCH Pounder-Kone' has amassed an enormous body of work including but not limited to video, theater, tv, film and video games.

Pounder married anthropologist Boubacar Kone' in 1991. The couple shared a passion for the arts and together they co-founded the Musee Boribana in Dakar, Senegal in 1993. It was the first museum of contemporary art in Dakar. The pair gifted the museum to the Senegalese people in 2014 and also joined forces to found the Pounder-Kone' Art Space in Los Angeles, California.

HISTORICAL HEROES CROSSWORD PUZZLE

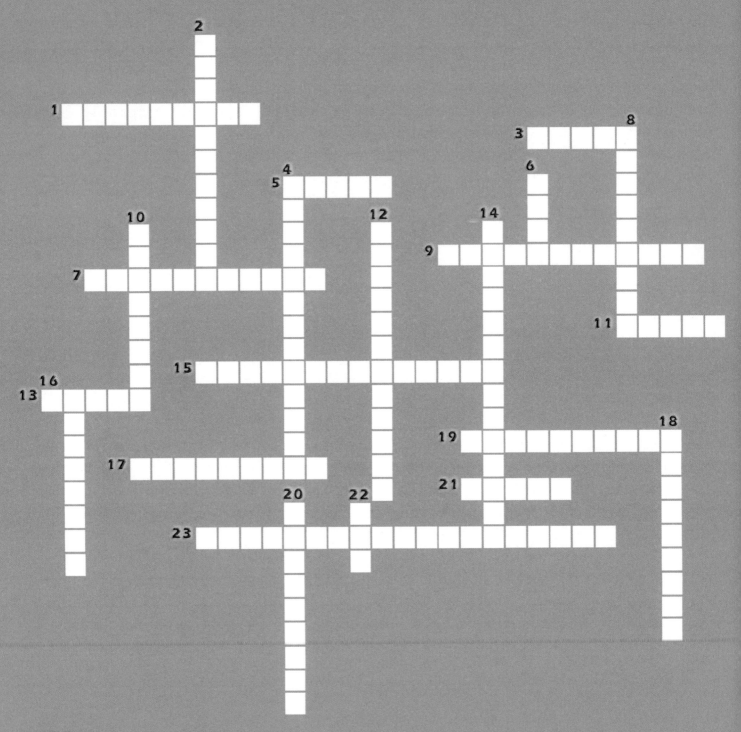

ACROSS

1. NAME THE SCHOOL LEONTYNE PRICE ATTENDED ON A FULL SCHOLARSHIP.

3. NAME OPRAH WINFREY'S PRODUCTION COMPANY AND STUDIO.

5. NAME OF BARACK AND MICHELLE OBAMA'S ELDEST DAUGHTER.

7. NAME THE MOST DECORATED AMERICAN GYMNAST.

9. WHAT FIELD OF MEDICINE DID DR. PATRICIA BATH STUDY?

PUZZLE CLUES

ACROSS CONT'D

11. HOW MANY EMMY NOMINATIONS DID WANDA SYKES WIN FOR HER OWN STAND-UP COMEDY SPECIAL?

13. HOW MANY GRAND SLAM TITLES DID VENUS WILLIAMS WIN?

15. WHICH PRESIDENT AWARDED LEONTYNE PRICE THE PRESIDENTIAL MEDAL OF FREEDOM?

17. FIRST BLACK FEMALE PERFORMER TO BE APPOINTED AS _____ DANCER FOR THE AMERICAN BALLET THEATRE.

19. WHAT KIND OF DISEASE WAS VENUS WILLIAMS DIAGNOSED WITH IN 2011.

21. FIRST BLACK FEMALE BILLIONAIRE IN THE US IN 2003.

23. SIMONE BILES JOINED THE CAST OF THE 24TH SEASON OF WHAT POPULAR TV SHOW?

DOWN

2. WHAT STYLE NETWORK DID NEICY NASH HOST FROM 2003-2010?

4. WHO WAS MARRIED TO THE 44TH PRESIDENT OF THE UNITED STATES?

6. WHAT PRESIDENT DID CONDOLEEZA RICE SERVE AS SECRETARY OF STATE UNDER?

8. WHAT IS THE NAME OF THE BOOK SERENA WILLIAMS PUBLISHED IN 2009?

10. NAME THE FIRST BLACK FEMALE ASTRONAUT IN SPACE.

12. NAME THE FIRST BLACK WOMAN TO WIN THE INDIVIDUAL ALL AROUND EVENT IN THE 2012 OLYMPICS.

14. OPRAH WINFREY STARRED IN WHAT FILM IN 1985?

16. MAE JEMISON FLEW INTO SPACE WITH SIX OTHER ASTRONAUTS ABOARD WHAT SPACECRAFT?

18. DR. PATRICIA BATH ESTABLISHED THAT _____ WAS A BASIC HUMAN RIGHT.

20. WHAT WAS MICHELLE OBAMA'S JOB FROM 2009-2017?

22. HOW MANY MIDDLE NAMES DOES GABBY DOUGLAS HAVE?

HISTORICAL HEROES
WORD SCRAMBLE

Directions: Unscramble the letters to find hidden clues. Decode circled letters to reveal the hidden message.

1. RD. RICIPATA THAB   _ _ (1)_ _ _ _ _ _ _   _ _ _ _ _

2. ZACNODOEEL ECRI   _ _ _ _ _ _ _ _ _ (2)_ _ _

3. AEM MIJENOS   _ _ _ _ _ _ (3)_ _

4. SUNVE NAD ERESNA   _ _ _ (4)_ _ _ _ _ _ _ _ _ _

5. TYSIM PENDLACO   _ _ _ _ _ _ _ _ _ _ _ _ (5)

6. TROASANUT   _ _ (6)_ _ _ _ _ _

7. CODIMEAN   _ (3)_ _ _ _ _ _

8. ELELMIHC MABAO   _ _ _ _ _ _ _ _ _ (7)_ _ _

9. ROPEA GRENIS   _ _ (8)_ _ _ _ _ _ _

10. IONBILLARIE   _ (7)_ _ _ _ _ _ _ _ _

11. BABYG LASOUDG   _ _ _ _ _ _ _ _ (9)_

12. BEALLIRNA   _ _ _ _ _ _ _ _ (10)

13. UTNCRKRECA   _ _ _ (11)_ _ _ _ _ _

14. KEYSS NDA SHAN   _ _ (12)_ _ _ _ _ _ _ _ _

15. YCRHEMTIS   _ _ (13)_ _ _ _ _ _

16. MEONIS LESIB   _ _ _ _ _ _ (14)_ _ _

17. PRTESIEDN   _ _ _ Ⓞ _ _ _ _ _

15

18. SETINN ROP   Ⓞ _ _ _ _ _ _   _ _ _ _

6

19. IOYMCSLP   Ⓞ _ _ _ _ _ _ _

3

20. HARPO NIWFEYR   _ _ _ _ _ _   _ _ _ _ Ⓞ _ _

2

21. TEONLYNE RICEP   _ _ _ _ _ _ Ⓞ _ _   _ _ _ _ _

16

22. SECTRAS   _ _ _ _ _ _ _

23. CHC RUNODEP-ONEK   _ _ _ _ _ _ _ _ _ _ _ _ - _ _ _ _ '

HIDDEN MESSAGE

_ _ _ _ _   _ _   _ _
1   2   3   4   5   6   3   7   8

_ _ _ _ _
7   9   10   11   12

_ _ _ _ _   _ _ _ _ _ _ _ _
7   9   10   11   12   13   14   15   6   3   2   16

REFLECTION QUESTIONS

1. NAME THE FIRST BLACK FIRST LADY MARRIED TO THE 44TH PRESIDENT? HOW MANY CHILDREN DID THEY HAVE AND WHAT ARE THEIR NAMES?

2. NAME THE TWO BLACK FEMALE OLYMPIC GYMNASTS YOU LEARNED ABOUT?

3. WHICH HISTORICAL BLACK WOMAN WAS AN ASTRONAUT?

4. NAME THE TWO BLACK FEMALE COMEDIANS YOU LEARNED ABOUT?

5. WHAT IS THE NAME FOR A DOCTOR WHO SPECIALIZES IN MEDICAL AND SURGICAL EYE PROBLEMS CALLED? WHAT IS THE NAME OF THE HISTORICAL BLACK FEMALE EYE DOCTOR YOU LEARNED ABOUT?

6. WHAT IS THE NAME OF THE FIRST BLACK FEMALE US SECRETARY OF STATE?

7. THIS HISTORICAL BLACK FEMALE BECAME A BILLIONAIRE WHO OWNED A TV NETWORK, A TALK SHOW AND HER OWN MAGAZINE?

8. NAME THE TWO BLACK FEMALE TENNIS PROFESSIONALS YOU LEARNED ABOUT? HOW WERE THEY RELATED?

9. WHICH HISTORICAL BLACK WOMAN WAS THE FIRST TO BE APPOINTED PRIMA BALLERINA BY ABT?

10. NAME THE WORLD FAMOUS BLACK FEMALE OPERA SINGER YOU LEARNED ABOUT.

11. WHAT IS THE NAME OF THE FAMOUS BLACK ACTRESS THAT IS CYDNEY-ELISE'S GRANDMA?

WHEN I GROW UP I WANT TO BE A:

_____

ACTION PLAN

STEPS TO ACHIEVING MY GOAL:

1. _____

2. _____

3. _____

4. _____

5. _____

IF YOU BELIEVE IN YOURSELF
AND FOLLOW YOUR DREAMS
YOU CAN ACHIEVE ANYTHING

HISTORICAL HEROES CROSSWORD PUZZLE ANSWER KEY

ACROSS
1 JUILLIARD
3 HARPO
5 MALIA
7 SIMONE BILES
9 OPHTHAMOLOGY
11 EIGHT
13 SEVEN

15 LYNDON B JOHNSON
17 PRINCIPAL
19 AUTOIMMUNE
21 OPRAH
23 DANCING WITH THE
      STARS

DOWN
2 CLEAN HOUSE
4 MICHELLE OBAMA
6 BUSH
8 ON THE LINE
10 JEMISON
12 GABBY DOUGLAS

14 THE COLOR PURPLE
16 ENDEAVOR
18 EYE SIGHT
20 FIRST LADY
22 TWO

HISTORICAL HEROES WORD SCRAMBLE ANSWER KEY

1 DR. PATRICIA BATH
2 CONDOLEEZA RICE
3 MAE JEMISON
4 VENUS AND SERENA
5 MISTY COPELAND
6 ASTRONAUT
7 COMEDIAN
8 MICHELLE OBAMA
9 OPERA SINGER
10 BILLIONAIRE
11 GABBY DOUGLAS

12 BALLERINA
13 NUTCRACKER
14 SYKES AND NASH
15 CHEMISTRY
16 SIMONE BILES
17 PRESIDENT
18 TENNIS PRO
19 OLYMPICS
20 OPRAH WINFREY
21 LEONTYNE PRICE
22 ACTRESS
23 CCH POUNDER KONE'

HISTORICAL HEROES WORD SCRAMBLE HIDDEN MESSAGE ANSWER KEY

- PROUD TO BE BLACK
* BLACK HISTORY

REFLECTION QUESTIONS ANSWER KEY

1. MICHELLE OBAMA
   TWO
   SACHA AND MALIA

2. GABBY DOUGLAS
   SIMONE BILES

3. MAE JEMISON

4. NEICY NASH
   WANDA SYKES

5. OPHTHALMOLOGY
   DR. PATRICIA BATH

6. CONDOLEEZA RICE

7. OPRAH WINFREY

8. VENUS WILLIAMS
   SERENA WILLIAMS
   SISTERS

9. MISTY COPELAND

10. LEONTYNE PRICE

11. CCH POUNDER-KONE'

Printed in the United States of America

First printing 2019

ISBN 9781092202053

4EVER4KIDS Publishing

Quantity sales and Special discounts available on quantity purchases by corporations, associations, and others. For information and details email 4ever4kids@gmail.com

Orders by U.S. trade bookstores and wholesalers please contact Ingram Spark Publishing

Made in the USA
Coppell, TX
11 March 2020